JOHNNY CASH

1932-2003

MEMORIAL SONGBOOK

Wise Publications

London / New York / Paris / Sydney / Copenhagen / Berlin / Madrid / Tokyo

Exclusive distributors:
Music Sales Limited
8/9 Frith Street, London W1D 3JB,
England.
Music Sales Pty Limited
120 Rothschild Avenue, Rosebery, NSW 2018,
Australia.

Order No. AM979099
ISBN 1-84449-333-4

Compiled by Nick Crispin.
Music arranged by Derek Jones & Lucy Holliday.
Music engraved by Paul Ewers Music Design.
Designed by Fresh Lemon.
Front cover photograph courtesy of Corbis.
Back cover photograph courtesy of Michael Ochs/Redferns.
Inside photographs courtesy of LFI, Redferns and Rex Features.

Printed in the United Kingdom by
Caligraving Limited, Thetford, Norfolk.

Johnny Cash

JOHNNY CASH
The Bedrock of Country Music

Johnny Cash, whose gravely bass-baritone was the vocal bedrock of American country music for more than four decades, died at the age of 71 on 12th September 2003 in Nashville. Known as the Man in Black, both for his voice, which projected the fateful gravity of a country patriarch, and for his signature look, which suggested a cowboy undertaker, Johnny Cash was one of the few performers who outlasted trends to become a mythical figure rediscovered by each new generation.

Beginning in the mid-1950's, when he made his first records for the Sun label, Johnny Cash forged a lean, hard-bitten country-folk music that at its most powerful seemed to erase the lines between singing, storytelling and gruelling life experience. Born in poverty in Arkansas at the height of the Depression, he was country music's foremost poet of the working poor. His stripped-down songs described the lives of coal miners and sharecroppers, convicts and cowboys, railroad workers and labourers.

Johnny Cash won 11 Grammy Awards including a lifetime achievement award in 1999. His influence extended far beyond the sphere of country music; along with Elvis Presley, Jerry Lee Lewis and Carl Perkins, his peers on Sun Records in the mid-1950's, he is considered a pioneer of rock 'n' roll. In 1992, 12 years after his election to the Country Music Hall of Fame, he was elected to the Rock and Roll Hall of Fame, and he remains the only performer besides Presley to have been inducted into both.

Rockers embraced him after he and Bob Dylan recorded a duet, *Girl From the North Country*, on Dylan's *Nashville Skyline* album. Recently, Johnny Cash's version of the Nine Inch Nails song *Hurt* won six nominations at the MTV Video Music Awards with the video winning Best Cinematography. Amongst numerous awards Johnny Cash won a total of 11 Grammys, including a lifetime achievement award in 1999.

'JR' Cash, the fourth of five siblings, born on February 26 to Ray and Carrie Cash in Kingsland, Arkansas,

1932

The Cash family moves to Dyess Colony on the Mississippi delta, where Ray works on a federal land-reclamation scheme. "The entire family, my parents, two brothers and two sisters spent the first night in the truck under a tarpaulin," Cash recalled.

1935

JR's elder brother Jack is killed in an accident with a circular saw in the lumber mill where he works. Johnny finds comfort in the Bible.

1944

Rock's Primal Beginnings

Unable to read music, Cash would compose a song in his head and play it over and over until he was satisfied enough to put it on tape. He would often write lyrics while travelling from one engagement to another.

The sounds of the slapped bass on his first major hit, *I Walk the Line*, and the hard-edged boom-chigga beat of the early hits he recorded with his trio, the Tennessee Three, were primal rock 'n' roll sounds. And his deep vocals, with their crags and quavers, demonstrated that a voice need not be pretty to be eloquent.

Cash's 1954 song about violent outcasts, *Folsom Prison Blues*, has even been described as a forerunner of gangsta rap. The song, which he wrote shortly after he left the Air Force, captured an essential ingredient of his mystique, the image of the reformed outlaw:

I hear that train a-comin'
Comin' round the bend.
I ain't seen the sunshine
Since I don't know when.
Well, I'm stuck in Folsom Prison
And time keeps draggin' on.

Johnny with Elvis, 1955

JR graduates from Dyess High School, heads north to Detroit, and finds work in a car-body factory in Pontiac, Michigan. However, he soon quits and signs up for the United States Air Force. He is posted to Germany where he learns to play guitar and write songs. He plays in a band called the Landsberg Barbarians. "We were terrible," he said later, "but that Lowenbrau beer will make you feel like you're great. I wrote Folsom Prison Blues in Germany in 1953."

1950

On August 7 he marries Vivian Liberto, whom he met while doing basic service training in Texas. The newly-weds move to Memphis where Cash becomes a door to door vacuum-cleaner salesman, and takes a course in radio announcing. His brother Ray introduced him to the Tennessee Three - Luther Perkins and Marshall Grant, plus AW "Red" Kernodle on steel guitar.

1954

After much rehearsal Cash signs with Sun Records in Memphis, who release his first single 'Hey Porter'. Sun Records boss Sam Phillips decides that from henceforth JR Cash will be known as Johnny Cash. In August Johnny makes his first big live appearance in Memphis, sharing a bill with Elvis Presley.

1955

Johnny in the 1950s

With its bare-bones realism, the song distilled the sepulchral grimness that often seemed to engulf Cash, who fought a long battle against addiction to drugs, particularly amphetamines. But he spent only one day in jail, in El Paso, for possession of pills that would have been legal with a prescription.

"There is that beast there in me," he said in an interview with Neil Strauss in The New York Times in 1994. "And I got to keep him caged, or he'll eat me alive." But as Strauss observed, the sinners that Cash sang about, unlike those in most gangsta raps, were usually plagued by guilt and seeking God's forgiveness. His tales may have been grim, but they were not nihilistic.

Johnny Cash's appeal transcended boundaries of class, generation and geography. Describing a characteristic performance, Paul Hemphill, a country music historian, once wrote: "Cash, wearing all black, Cash with human suffering in his deep eyes and on his tortured face, Cash, insolent and lashing out from the stage, Cash, in a black swallowtail coat and striped morning pants like an elegant undertaker, Cash swinging his guitar around, pointing it at his listeners as though it were a tommy gun, all of these things captured the whole world."

Cash quits his day job and in May Sun releases 'I Walk The Line', his first national hit. In December he is photographed at Sun studios alongside Elvis, Jerry Lee Lewis and Carl Perkins – the 'million dollar quartet'.

1956

Cash's only Sun album *Johnny Cash With His Hot And Blue Guitar*, is released.

1957

Johnny's more pop-orientated 'Ballad Of A Teenage Queen' reaches number 14 on the national charts, his biggest hit for Sun but Sam Phillips decides he'd prefer to drop Cash instead of increasing the rising star's royalty rate. Johnny signs with CBS, simultaneously transplanting his band, family and manager to Los Angeles.

1958

In a career in which he recorded more than 1,500 songs, he applied his gritty voice to almost every kind of material. Blues, hymns, cowboy songs, American Indian ballads, railroad songs, children's songs, spoken narratives, patriotic songs, love songs and novelties were all delivered in a near-monotone that was the vocal equivalent of a monument hammered out of stone.

Johnny Cash's stoical singing about loneliness and death, love and humble Christian faith reflected the barren terrain of his upbringing. He was born in a shack on February 26, 1932, in Kingsland, Arkansas, to Ray Cash and Carrie Rivers Cash, cotton farmers whose livelihood was destroyed by the Depression. They named him J. R.; it is not clear how John evolved, and the R is a mystery. But it was the legendary record producer Sam Phillips of Sun Records who later gave him the name Johnny.

Johnny with guest Bob Dylan on *The Johnny Cash Show*

Cash's first album for CBS *The Fabulous Johnny Cash* is his first to make the national album charts. Hit singles are not long in coming, in the shape of 'Don't Take Your Guns To Town', 'I Got Stripes', 'Five Feet High And Rising' and 'The Ballad Of Johnny Yuma'.

1959

Cash plays the first of his celebrated prison shows at San Quentin, where one of the inmates yelling him on is Merle Haggard, imprisoned on a burglary charge.

1960

'Ring Of Fire', co-written by Merle haggard and June Carter climbs to number 17 in the pop charts. Carter and Cash begin playing together as a duo.

1963

From Air Force to Star

Drawn to country music on the radio, young J. R. Cash listened to the Grand Ole Opry and particularly admired the music of Ernest Tubb, Roy Acuff, Hank Williams and the Carter Family. He began writing songs, poems and stories and sang on local radio in Arkansas. When he was 12, his faith deepened after his older brother Jack, a preacher, was killed in an accident.

Following his high school graduation, he headed north and took a job at an auto body plant in Pontiac, Michigan. The job lasted less than a month, and he enlisted in the Air Force in 1950. He was sent to Landsberg, Germany, where he served as a radio operator and was promoted to staff sergeant.

Johnny with wife June Carter and Carl Perkins

As the Sixties unfold, Johnny is obliged to play up to 300 concerts a year, and finds himself becoming increasingly dependent on amphetamines to keep going, even though he knows they affect his writing and records.

1963

Cash shows his political side by releasing *Bitter Tears*, subtitled *Ballads Of The American Indian*, a collection of Indian protest songs which includes his memorable treatment of Pete LaFarge's 'Ballad Of Ira Hayes'.

1964

Cash's amphetamine habit reaches crisis point when he is jailed for three days after being arrested in El Paso, smuggling amphetamines into the US across the Mexican border. This same year he inadvertently starts a forest fire which burns up 508 acres in California and costs him an $85,000 fine.

1965

On returning to the United States in 1954 he met a pair of guitar-playing auto mechanics, Monroe Perkins and Marshall Grant, who with the steel guitarist A. W. Kernodle became the members of his first band, which performed at church socials and country fairs.

In late 1954, the band, minus Kernodle, who had left, auditioned for Sam Phillips, and the following spring the group, the Tennessee Three, recorded five songs for Sun. Cash was signed to a contract by Sun and began to tour the United States and Canada and appear on radio and television.

In May 1956, Sun released Johnny Cash's biggest hit and signature song, *I Walk the Line*, a stern avowal of sexual fidelity that eventually sold more than two million copies. His next single, *There You Go*, also reached No. 1 on the country charts, and in July he was invited to join the Grand Ole Opry. By the summer of 1958, he had written more than 50 songs, and he had sold more than six million records for Sun. But when the label balked at letting Cash record gospel music, he moved to Columbia Records, where he would remain for the next 28 years.

The Johnny Cash retrospective film – *Johnny Cash The Man His World His Music*, 1969

His career took a sharp upswing in the late 1960's. He released two hugely successful albums, *At Folsom Prison* and *At San Quentin*. His association with Bob Dylan, whom he had befriended at the Newport Folk Festival in 1964, helped to bring his music to a young rock audience. In 1968 he filled Carnegie Hall and broke the Beatles' attendance record at the Palladium in London.

1967

On tour in Georgia, Cash is found near death from amphetamine abuse. Vivian, now the mother of his four daughters (including singer-to-be Rosanne) divorces him. Johnny and June Carter score a hit with their duet version of 'Jackson'.

1968

In March Johnny and June marry after he proposes to her on stage. "The love that John and I share with our love for Christ is one of the most precious gifts God could have given us," she would later write. The album *Johnny Cash At Folsom Prison* is a huge success and is still widely regarded as one of the finest country records ever made.

1969

The *Johnny Cash Show* debuts on ABC-TV. Based in Nashville, the show will pull in artists from every conceivable genre, highlighting the breadth of Cash's tastes. Cash befriends Bob Dylan which leads to them duetting on 'Girl From The North Country', on Dylan's 1969 country album *Nashville Skyline*, for which Cash also writes sleeve notes. *Johnny Cash At San Quentin* becomes Cash's only number 1 album in the US and spawns an international hit single with the tongue-in-cheek 'A Boy Named Sue'.

By 1969, Johnny Cash was the host of his own network television show, appearing over the next two years with stars like Bob Dylan, Glen Campbell, Ray Charles and the Carter Family. Also in 1969, his novelty song *A Boy Named Sue*, written by Shel Silverstein, became his biggest pop hit.

Johnny Cash, like many other older stars who had achieved an almost statesmanlike status in the country music firmament, experienced some decline in record sales in the 1980's and 90's. After leaving Columbia, he signed in 1986 with Mercury, where he had limited success. But if his career flagged, his legend flourished.

Johnny with guitar at his home in Tennessee

In August Cash performs for President Nixon at the White House.

1970

Cash releases his *Man In Black* album, stating: "I wear the black for the poor and the beaten down, living in the hopeless, hungry side of town. I wear it for the prisoner who has long paid for his crime..."

1971

Cash joins evangelist Billy Graham on stage at Wembley Stadium in London and sings a duet with Cliff Richard.

1973

The Johnny Cash Show **with Roy Orbison, Carl Perkins, Jerry Lee Lewis and friends, 1970**

Throughout the Seventies Cash cements his persona as American icon and man of integrity. His commanding presence leads to screen appearances in the western series *Rawhide*, and with Kirk Douglas in *A Gunfight* (1972). He also appears in a string of TV movies.

With the music from Nashville softening into middle-of-the-road, sugar-coated escapism, Cash becomes alienated from the country establishment who fail to appreciate him as a veteran of the tough Sun era. He continues to tour as the star of the Carter Family Roadshow, almost always closing the shows with the traditional song 'Will The Circle be Unbroken', surrounded by June and her sisters.

1973

Cash is inducted into the Country Music Hall Of Fame.

1980

June and Johnny with Marie Osmond And Robert Duvall, 1991

Cash teams up with Willie Nelson, Waylon Jennings and Kris Kristofferson to form the successful recording and touring outfit, The Highwaymen.

1985

Columbia end their 28-year relationship with the Cash – arguably one of the most short-sighted blunders in the history of the record industry, and it rankles with Cash – not least because this same year *Johnny Cash at Folsom Prison*, *Johnny Cash at San Quinten* and *Johnny Cash's Greatest Hits* are all certified two million sellers.

1986

Johnny signs with Mercury and debuts with the album *Johnny Cash Is Coming To Town* which includes the live favourite 'The Night Hank Williams Came To Town'.

1987

The Highwaymen - Waylon Jennings, Willie Nelson, Kris Kristofferson and Johnny

Cash undergoes double heart bypass surgery in Nashville which partially prompts the UK Red Rhino label to issue *'Til Things Are Brighter*, which features young artists – including Michelle Skocked, Brendon Crocker and The Mekons – covering Cash songs to raise money for Aids research.

1988

Cash is inducted into the Rock'n'Roll Hall Of Fame, thus becoming the only the second artist after Elvis Presley to be inducted into both the Country and Rock halls of fame. In October he performs 'It Ain't Me Babe' with June at the Bob Dylan 30th Anniversary celebration at New York's Madison Square Garden.

1992

Cash's deep baritone is featured on 'The Wanderer', from U2's *Zooropa* album

1993

A 90's Comeback

The musical career of Johnny Cash took an unusual turn in 1994 when he was signed by Rick Rubin, a producer of heavy metal and rap acts, to Rubin's label, American Records. *American Recordings*, his first album for the label, was a bare-bones country-folk album in which he applied his fatalistic stamp to songs by Tom Waits, Leonard Cohen, Loudon Wainwright III and other folk-pop songwriters. The album sold only a little more than 100,000 copies, but it won him his sixth Grammy Award, in the best contemporary folk album category.

1994

The *American Recordings* album, produced by Def Jam rap/metal supreme Rick Rubin for his Def American label, leads to a complete reappraisal of the legend of Johnny Cash, and one which finds a new audience. He appears at the Glastonbury Festival on the Sunday afternoon 'veterans' slot to a rousing ovation from a new, young audience.

1995

American Recordings wins Best Contemporary Folk album at the Grammy Awards.

1996

A second album on the American label, *Unchained*, is released, featuring vintage country tunes by Jimmie Rodgers and the Louvin Brothers with "alternative rock" songs from Soundgarden and Beck.

For all the grimness of his Man in Black persona, Johnny Cash insisted that he was not a morbid person. "I am not obsessed with death — I'm obsessed with living," he said in 1994, six years after recovering from heart surgery. "The battle against the dark one and the clinging to the right one is what my life is about."

In *Cash*, his second autobiography, written with Patrick Carr and published in 1997, he fantasised about the final word on Johnny Cash, when "halfway through *Ring of Fire* or *I Still Miss Someone* or *Sunday Morning Coming Down*, I'll just keel over and die on the stage, under the lights, with my band and my family around me. That's every performer's dream, you know."

Johnny with June in 1996

Cash wins a Lifetime Achievement award at the Grammies, the 11th Grammy of his career.

1999

The Man Comes Around, Cash's fourth album for American, earns rapturous critical acclaim for outstanding covers of 'Bridge Over Troubled Water', 'Desperado' and Depeche Mode's 'Personal Jesus'. Cash's version of the Nine Inch Nails song 'Hurt' is turned into an introspective career-topping video and is nominated for six MTV awards, winning one for cinematography.

2002

In May June Carter Cash died from complications following heart surgery. To mark what would have been her 74th birthday, on June 21, Johnny appears at the Carter Fold, in the Virginia Mountains. He is helped on stage by family members and is able to manage a few songs before being taken home to rest. "I don't hardly know what what to say about being up here without her," he says. "The pain is so severe there is no way of describing it."

Cash continues to record right up his death on September 12.

2003

Big River

Words & Music by Johnny Cash

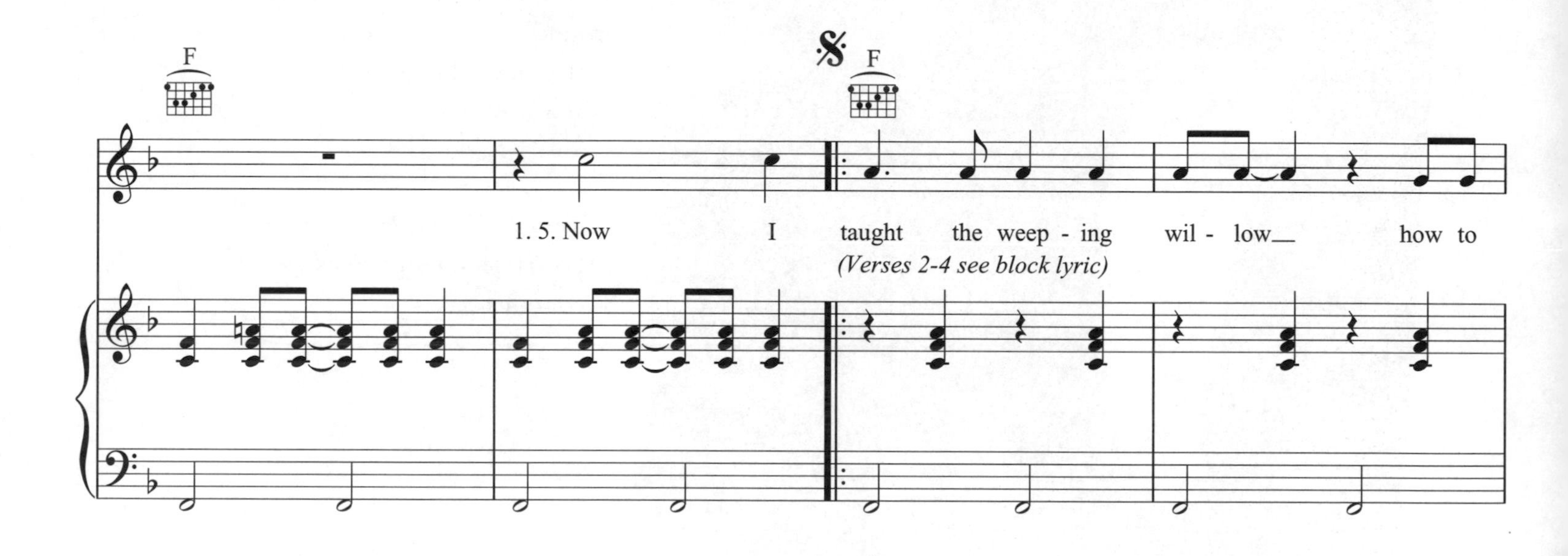

G7
C7
F
3fr
clear, blue sky. And the tears that I cried for that wo - man are gon - na
B♭
To Coda
F
C7
flood you big riv - er, then I'm gon - na sit right here un - til I
1, 3.
2, 4.
Fm
F5
die.
2. I call.
F5
Fm
F5
B♭

Verse 2:
I met her accidentally in St Paul, Minnesota,
And it tore me up every time I heard her drawl, Southern drawl.
Then I heard my dream was back downstream, cavortin' in Davenport,
And I followed you big river, when you called.

Verse 3:
Then you took me to St, Louis later on down the river.
A freighter said she's been here
But she's gone, boy, she's gone.
I found her trail in Memphis,
But she just walked up the block.
She raised a few eyebrows and then she went on down alone.

Verse 4:
Now, won't you batter down by Baton Rouge,
River Queen, roll it on.
Take that woman on down to New Orleans, New Orleans.
Go on, I've had enough;
Dump my blues down in the gulf.
She loves you, big river, more than me.

A Boy Named Sue

Words & Music by Shel Silverstein

F7
B♭
-fore he left, he went and named me Sue.
Well he must have thought it was quite a joke, and it got a lot of laughs from a
E♭
3fr
F7
B♭
lot of folks. It seems I had to fight my whole life through.
E♭
3fr
Some gal would giggle and I'd get red, and some guy would laugh and I'd

Verse 2:
(Well,) I grew up quick and I grew up mean. My fist got hard and my wits got keen.
Roamed from town to town to hide my shame, but I made me a vow to the moon and stars,
I'd search the honky tonks and bars and kill that man that give me that awful name.
But it was Gatlinburg in mid July and I had just hit the town and my throat was dry,
I thought I'd stop and have myself a brew. At an old saloon on a street of mud
There at a table dealing stud sat the dirty, mangy dog that named me Sue.

Verse 3:
Well I knew that snake was my own sweet dad from a worn out picture that my mother had had.
And I know that scar on his cheek and his evil eye. He was big and bent and grey and old
And I looked at him hard and my blood ran cold, and I said "My name is Sue. How do you do.
Now you're gonna die." Yeah, that's what I told him.
Well I hit him hard right between the eyes and he went down, but to my surprise he came up with a knife
And cut off a piece of my ear. But I busted a chair right across his teeth, and we crashed through
The wall and into the street, kicking and a-gouging in the mud and the blood and the beer.

Verse 4:
I tell you I've fought tougher men but I really can't remember when,
He kicked like a mule and he bit like a crocodile. I heard him laughin' and then him cussin',
He went for his gun and I pulled mine first. He stood there looking at me and I saw him smile,
And he said "Son, this world is rough and if a man's gonna make it, he's gotta be tough
And I know I wouldn't be there to help you along. So I give you that name and I said 'Goodbye,'
I knew you'd have to get tough or die. And it's that name that helped to make you strong."

Verse 5:
Yeah, "He said now you just fought one helluva fight, and I know you hate me and you've
Got the right to kill me now and I wouldn't blame you if you do. But you ought to thank me
Before I die for the gravel in your guts and the spit in your eye because I'm the son of a bitch
That named you Sue."
Yeah, what could I do? What could I do?
I got all choked up and I threw down my gun. Called him my pa and he called me his son,
And I come away with a different point of view. And I think about him now and then.
Every time I tried, every time I win and if I ever have a son I think I'm gonna name him
Bill or George, any damn thing but Sue'.

Folsom Prison Blues

Words & Music by Johnny Cash

Verse 4:
I bet there's rich folks eatin' in a fancy dining car.
They're prob'ly drinkin' coffee and smokin' big cigars,
But I know I had it comin', I know I can't be free,
But those people keep a-movin', and that's what tortures me.

Verse 5: Instrumental

Verse 6:
Well, if they freed me from prison, if that railroad train was mine,
I bet I'd move it on a little further down the line,
Far from Folsom Prison, that's where I want to stay,
And I'd let that lonesome whistle blow my blues away.

Get Rhythm

Words & Music by Johnny Cash

B♭
C
F
rhy - thm, when you get the blues.
1. A lit - tle
2. Well I
shoe shine boy he nev - er gets low down but he's got the dir - ti - est
sat and I lis - tened to the shoe shine boy and I thought I was gonna
job in town, bend - ing low at the peo - ples feet on a
jump for joy, slapped on the shoe po - lish left and right, he took the
wind - y cor - ner of a dir - ty street. When I asked him while he
shoe shine rag and he held it tight. He stopped once to wipe the

shined my shoe how'd he keep from get - ting the blues? He
sweat a - way, I said you mighty lit - tle boy to be a - work - ing that way. He
grinned as he raised his lit - tle head, he popped his shoe - shine rag and
said I like it with a big wide grin kept on a - pop - ping and
then he said, get rhy - thm when you get the blues,
he say it again get rhy - thm when you get the blues,
B♭
come on get rhy - thm when you get the blues,
come on get rhy - thm when you get the blues,

F
a jump - ing rhy - thm makes you feel so fine it - 'll
it only cost a dime just a nickle a shoe it does a
B♭
To Coda
shake all your trou - ble from your wor - ried mind, get rhy - thm
mil - lion dol - lars worth of good for you, get rhy - thm
C
F
when you get the blues.
when you get the blues.
B♭

F
B♭
C
F
D.S. al Coda
Coda
C
Get
when you
get the blues.
F

Hurt

Words & Music by Trent Reznor

Am
C
Dsus2
Am
C
Dsus2
real. The nee - dle tears a hole, the old fa - mil - iar sting.
-pair. Be - neath the stains of time the feel - ings dis - ap - pear.
Am
C
Dsus2
Am
C
D
Try to kill it all a - way but I re - mem - ber ev - 'ry - thing.
You are some - one else, I am still right here.
G
Am7
Fadd9
What have I be - come
C
G
Am7
my sweet - est friend? Ev - 'ry - one I know

Fadd9
C
G
goes a - way in the end. And
Am7
Fadd9
G
you could have it all, my em - pire of dirt.
Am7
Fadd9
I will let you down,
1.
G
Am
C
D
I will make you hurt.

2.
Am
C
Dsus2
G
I will make you hurt.
Am7
Fadd9
If I could start a - gain, a
G
Am7
mil - lion miles a - way,
I would keep my - self,
Fadd9
G
I would find a way.

YAMAHA
NS-10M STUDIO

UNIVERSAL AUDIO
Technics
TASCAM DA-30
ALESIS
adat

Girl From The North Country

Words & Music by Bob Dylan

Verse 2:
See for me that her hair's hanging down.
It curls and falls all down her breast.
See for me, that her hair's hanging down,
That's the way I remember her best.

Verse 3:
If you go where the snowflakes fall,
When the rivers freeze, and summer ends
Please see for me if she's wearing a coat so warm
To keep her from the howling winds.

Verse 4:
If you're travelling in the north country fair
Where the winds hit heavy on the borderline.
Please say hello to the one who lives there,
For she once was a true love of mine.

I Still Miss Someone

Words & Music by Johnny Cash & Roy Cash

E♭
F
Sweet hearts walk by to - geth - er, and
find a dark - ened corn - er 'cause
E♭
F
B♭
1.
I still miss some - one. 2. I
I still miss some - one.
2.
E♭
F
B♭
No, I nev - er got ov - er those blue eyes,
E♭
F
B♭
I see them ev - 'ry - where. I

E♭
F
B♭
E♭
miss those arms that held me when all the
F
B♭
B♭
E♭
love was there. I won - der if she's
F
E♭
F
B♭
sor - ry for leav - ing what we'd be - gun.
B♭
E♭
F
There's some - one for me some - where and

E♭
F
B♭
To Coda
I still miss some - one.
F6
E♭
(I still
miss some - one.)
No, I
D.S. al Coda
Coda
rit.
- one.
(I still miss some - one.)

I Walk The Line

Words & Music by Johnny Cash

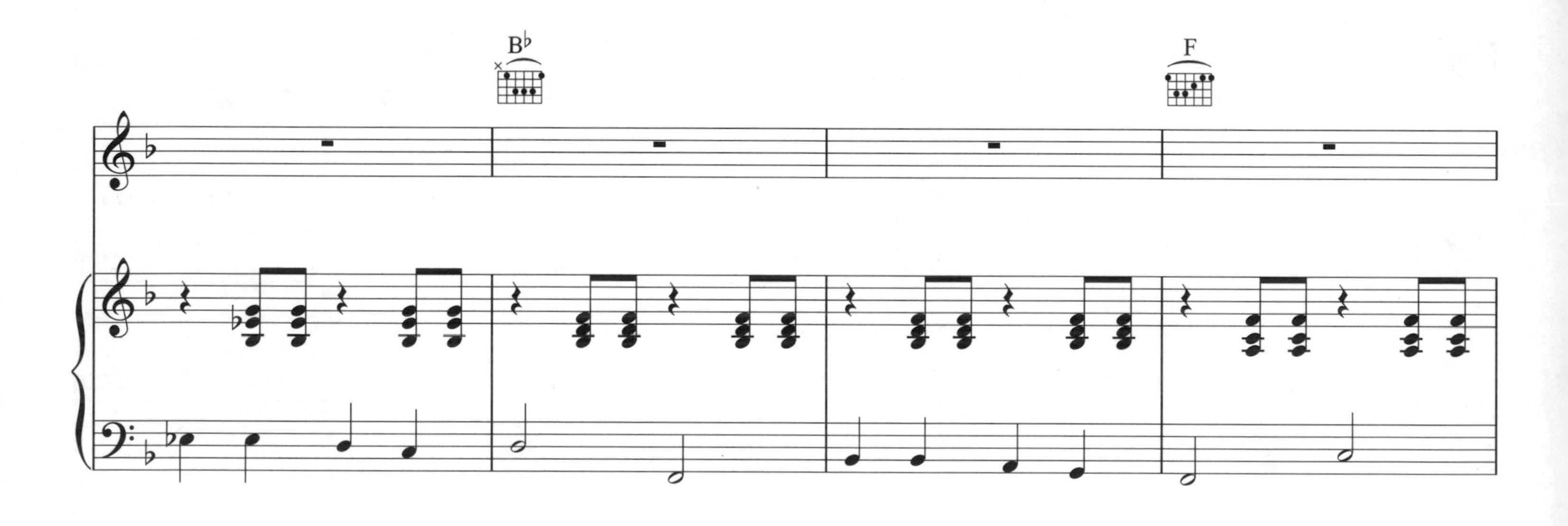

Mmm.
1. I keep a
C7
3fr
F
close watch on this heart of mine.
I keep my
C7
3fr
F
eyes wide op - en all the time.
I keep the

B♭
F
ends out for the tie that binds, be - cause you're
C7
3fr
F
mine, I walk the line.
B♭
Mmm.
2. I find it
4. You've got a

F
B♭
ve - ry, ve - ry ea - sy to be true. I find my -
way to keep me on your side. You give me
F
B♭
- self a - lone when each day is through. Yes I'll ad -
cause for love that I can't hide. For you I
E♭
6fr
B♭
- mit that I'm a fool for you, be - cause you're
know I'd ev - en try to turn the tide, be - cause you're
F
B♭
To Coda
mine, I walk the line.
mine, I walk the line.

E♭
6fr
Mmm.
3. As sure as
B♭
E♭
6fr
night is dark and day is light.
I keep you
B♭
E♭
6fr
on my mind both day and night.
And hap - pi -

A♭
4fr
E♭
6fr
-ness I've known proves that it's right, be - cause you're
B♭
E♭
6fr
B♭
D.S. al Coda
mine, I walk the line.
Coda
F
Mm.
5. I keep a

C7
3fr
F
close watch on this heart of mine. I keep my
C7
3fr
F
eyes wide op - en all the time. I keep the
B♭
F
8vb
ends out for the tie that binds, be - cause you're
C7
3fr
F
(8)
Repeat to fade
mine, I walk the line. Mmm.

The Night Hank Williams Came To Town

Words & Music by Charlie Williams & Bobby Braddock

E
I was still in love
'Cause no - one stayed at home
A
with Ma - vis Brown
for miles a - round.
E
on the night Hank
It was the night Hank
B7
E
Wil - liams came to town.
Wil - liams came to town.
1.
2.
E
E7
A
3. Ma - ma ironed my shirt and Dad - dy

E
F#7
let me take the truck. I drove on up to Grape -
B
- vine and picked old Ma - vis up. We hit
E
A
that coun - ty line for one quick round
E
B7
on the night Hank Wil - liams came to town.

E
E
4. A thou - sand peo - ple swel - tered in the gym,
A
B7
then I heard some - one whis - per "Hey that's him."
E
That's when the crowd let out this deaf - en - ing
A
E
B7
sound. It was the night Hank Wil - liams came to town.

E
N.C.
G
C
5. On and on he sang in - to the night,
'Jam - bal - ay - a' 'Cheat - in' Heart' 'I Saw The Light'.
D7
G
And
C
how'd they get Miss Aud - rey in the gown,

G
D7
G
on the night Hank Wil - liams came to town?
Guitar
C
G
D
G
N.C.
C
G
(8)
6. Ma - vis had her pic - ture made with Hank out by his car. She
7. Hank signed his au - to - graph on Beau - lah Rice's fan.

A7
D
said "He sure is hum - ble for a Grand Ole Op - ry star."
Ma - vis got a - quain - ted with the Drift - ing Cow - boy's band. The ef -
G
C
1.
Ma - vis said "Why don't we hang a - round, it ain't of -
- fect on all our lives was quite pro - found,
G
D7
G
- ten that Hank Wil - liams comes to town." While
2. Free time
C
G
D7
G a tempo
on the night Hank Wil - liams came to town.

G
G7
Instrumental & Vocal ad lib.
C
G
D7
G
Repeat ad lib. to fade

Ring Of Fire

Words & Music by June Carter & Merle Kilgore

D7
G
C
and it makes a fi - ry ring.
when hearts like ours beat.

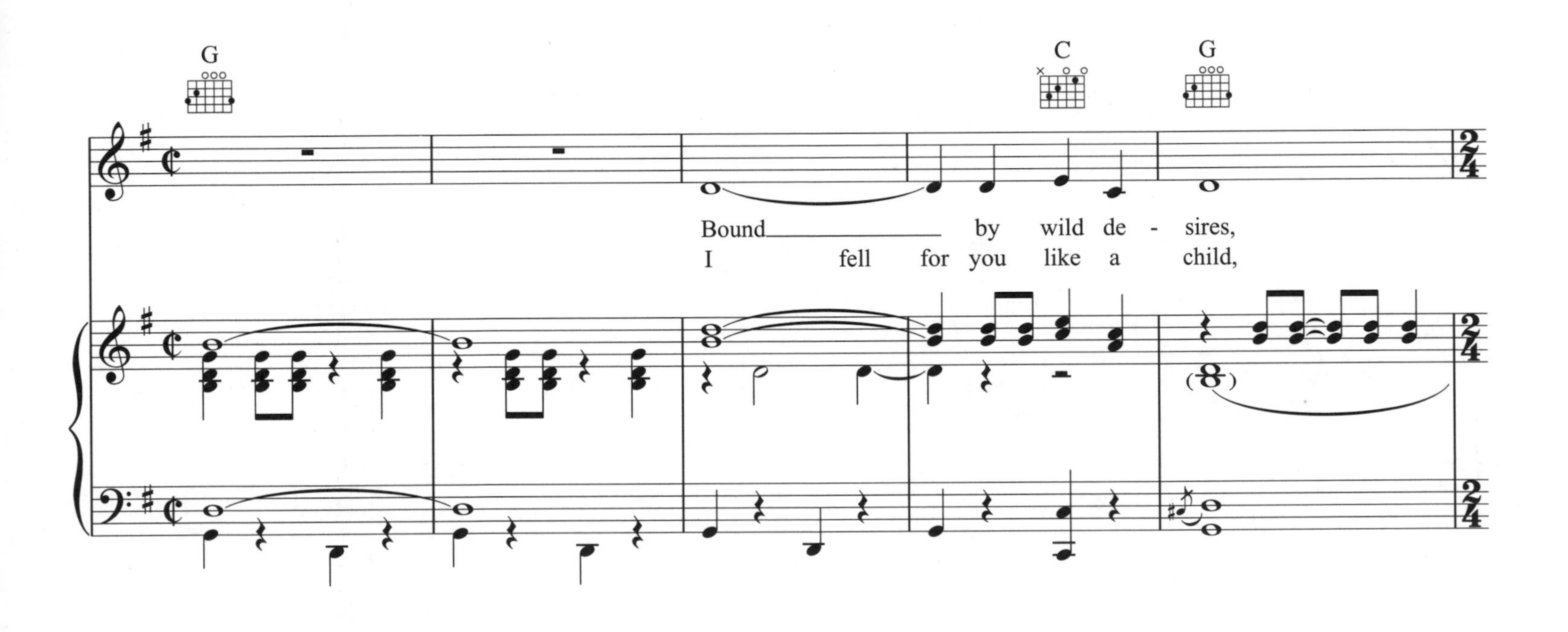
G
C
G
Bound by wild de - sires,
I fell for you like a child,

C
G
D7
I fell in to a ring of
oh but the fire went

G
D7
C
fire.
wild.
I fell in to a burn-ing ring of

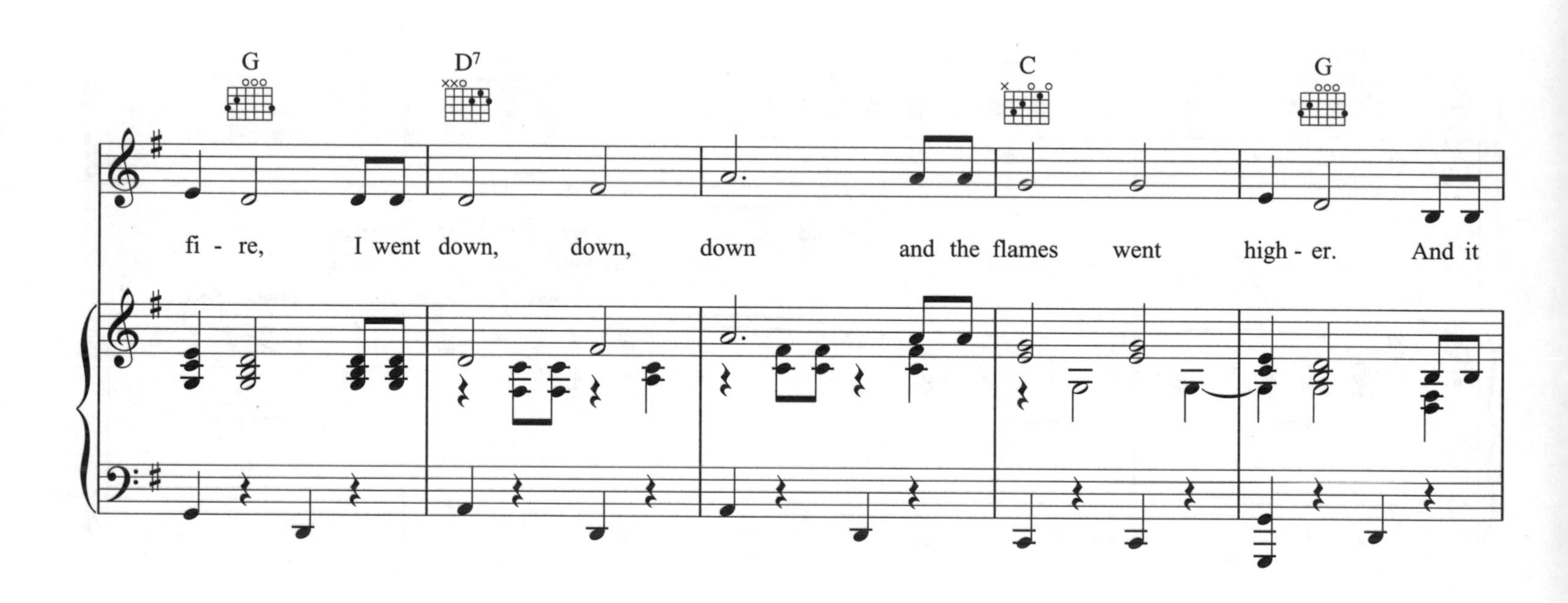
G
D7
C
G
fi - re, I went down, down, down and the flames went high - er. And it

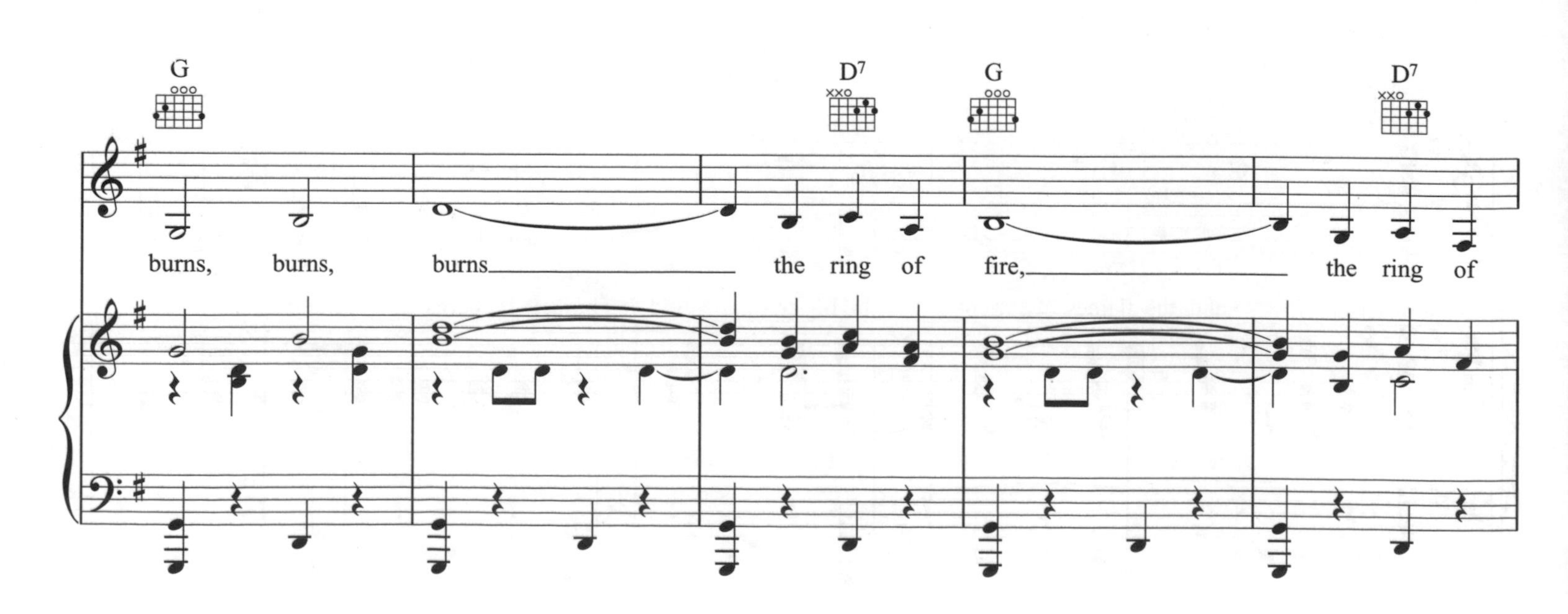
G
D7
G
D7
burns, burns, burns the ring of fire, the ring of

G
To Coda
C
G
fire.
D7
I fell in to a burn - ing ring of fi - re, I went down, down,
down and the flames went high - er. And it burns, burns, burns

D7
G
D7
G
— the ring of fire,
the ring of fire.
The
Coda
D7
C
G
I fell in to a burn - ing ring of fi - re, I went

D7
C
G
down, down, down and the flames went high - er. And it burns, burns,

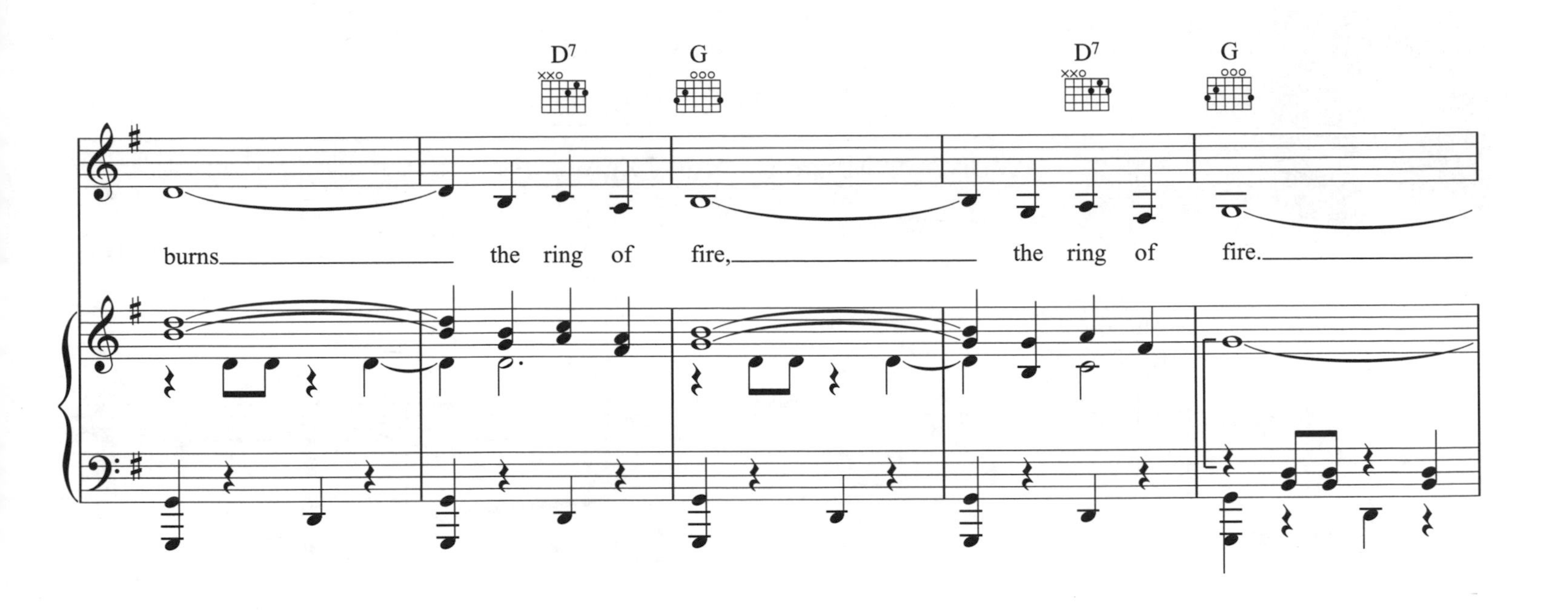
D7
G
D7
G
burns
the ring of fire,
the ring of fire.

D7
and it burns, burns, burns
the ring of

G
Repeat and fade
fire,
the ring of fire.
The ring of

Solitary Man

Words & Music by Neil Diamond

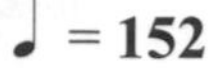

Cm
3fr
Gm
3fr
Cm
3fr
Then Sue came a - long, loved me strong,
I know it's been done hav - in' one
B♭
Gm
3fr
B♭
that's what I thought. Me and Sue,
girl who loved me, right or wrong,
Cm
3fr
B♭
Cm
3fr
but that died, too.
weak or strong.
B♭
E♭
3fr
1. Don't know that I will, but un - til
2. Don't know that I will, but un - til
(D.S.) Don't know that I will, but un - til

B♭
F
F9
7fr
F
— I can find me a girl who'll
— love can find me and the girl who'll
— love can find me and the girl who'll
E♭
3fr
B♭
F
stay and won't play games be - hind me, I'll
Gm
3fr
F
— be what I am, a so - li - ta - ry man,
Gm
3fr
F
To Coda
Gm
3fr
— a so - li - ta - ry man.

1.
I've had it to here
2.
Cm
3fr
Guitar solo
Gm
3fr
Cm
3fr
D.S. al Coda
Coda
Gm
3fr
Fadd9
7fr
Gm
3fr
So - li - ta - ry man.

The Wanderer

Words & Music by U2

F♯
skin and bones___ of a ci - ty with - out a soul.___
-dom but they don't want God in it.___
- vy on my heart,__ I was sure I was___ the one.___ Now

F♯
I went out walk - ing un - der an a - tom - ic sky___
I went out rid - ing down that old eight
Je - sus, don't you wait up. Je - sus I'll be home soon.___

Badd9
___ where the ground won't turn and the rain, it burns___ like the
lane I passed by a thou - sand signs___
___ Yeah, I went out___ for the pa - pers,

F♯
D♯m
tears when I said good - bye.
look - ing for my own name.
told her I'd be back by noon.
Yeah, I went with
I went with
Yeah, I left with
Bmaj7
F♯
C♯6
2fr
no - thing no - thing but the thought of you. I went wan -
no - thing, but the thought you'd be there too, look - ing for
no - thing, but the thought you'd be there too, look - ing for
D♯m
Bmaj7
C♯sus4
4fr
F♯
To Coda
- der - ing.
you.
you.

1.
F♯
2. I went drift - ing through the ca-pi - tals of tin where men
Badd9
can't walk or free-ly talk and sons turn their fa-thers in. I stopped
F♯
2.
F♯
3
Guitar
B/F♯
F♯
Spoken: I went out there in search of experience. To taste

D#m
Bmaj7
F#
and to touch
and to feel as much
as a man can
C#6
2fr
D#m
Bmaj7
C#sus4
4fr
before he repents.
F#
F#
3. I went out search -
- ing,
look - ing for one good man.
A

Badd9
F♯
spi - rit who would not bend or break, who would sit at his fa - ther's right
D.S. al Coda
Coda
D♯m
Bmaj7
hand.
Yeah, I left with no - thing,
F♯
C♯6
2fr
D♯m
no - thing but the thought of you. I went wan - der - ing.
Bmaj7
C♯sus4
4fr
F♯
D.SS. Instrumental to fade